RHYMES ON FIRE

Edited By Roseanna Caswell

First published in Great Britain in 2022 by:

 Young**Writers**® Est. 1991

Young Writers
Remus House
Coltsfoot Drive
Peterborough
PE2 9BF
Telephone: 01733 890066
Website: www.youngwriters.co.uk

Printed and bound in the UK by BookPrintingUK
Website: www.bookprintinguk.com
YB0491Q

FOREWORD

*For Young Writers' latest competition This Is Me,
we asked primary school pupils to look inside
themselves, to think about what makes them unique,
and then write a poem about it! They rose to the
challenge magnificently and the result is this fantastic
collection of poems in a variety of poetic styles.*

*Here at Young Writers our aim is to encourage creativity
in children and to inspire a love of the written word, so
it's great to get such an amazing response, with some
absolutely fantastic poems. It's important for children to
focus on and celebrate themselves and this competition
allowed them to write freely and honestly, celebrating
what makes them great, expressing their hopes and
fears, or simply writing about their favourite things.
This Is Me gave them the power of words. The result
is a collection of inspirational and moving poems that
also showcase their creativity and writing ability.*

*I'd like to congratulate all the young poets
in this anthology, I hope this inspires them
to continue with their creative writing.*

CONTENTS

Oliver Dyson (10)	57
Amelie Barker (9)	58
Szymon Olszewski (11)	59
Lydia Brown (7)	60
Ruby Mullen (11)	61
Luca Drinkwater (9)	62
Eloise Ireson (10)	63
Rihanna Vera Cruz (10)	64
Emmeline Illston (11)	65
Lois Cox (9)	66
Hayden Golder (9)	67
Evie-May Brown (10)	68
Ellen Johnson (9)	69
Alex Pedlar (10)	70
Sonny Collins (9)	71
Kate-Lynn Doyle (7)	72
Isabell Kyle (9)	73
Thillali Boussaid (9)	74
Riley Virgo (9)	75
Archie Tyler (10)	76
Matthew Hale (10)	77
Anusha Jackson (9)	78
Tabitha Forde (9)	79
Farah Eccleston (9)	80
Ryan Philpotts (10)	81
Danniel Choudhury (10)	82
Zeva B-H	83
Edie Pinder (9)	84
Kaycie Evans (9)	85
Phoebe Wiggett (9)	86
Ben Rusling	87
Benjamin Powles (10)	88
Samuel Cutts (10)	89
Kaiden Pearce (10)	90
Richie Smith (9)	91
Poppy Whakahau (9)	92
Alfie Tedds (9)	93
Thomas Summerfield (10)	94
Faith (9)	95
Ellie Mitchell (10)	96
Anna Jones (9)	97
Harriet Perkins (9)	98

Pomphlett Primary School, Plymstock

Addison Flewin (9)	99
Harriet Abbott (9)	100
Maddison Mather (9)	101
Willow Gordon (7)	102
Stevie Hopkin (10)	103
Chloe Kelly (10)	104

Robert Gordon's College, Aberdeen

Antonina Weychan (9)	105
Isla Clark (10)	106
Kosi Ileagu (10)	108
Charles Leroy (10)	110
Andrew Hendrie (10)	112
Ryan Knox (9)	114
Ryan Lees (10)	116
Lucas Baird (10)	118
Lilia Sheed (10)	120
Renée De Kock (9)	122
Ireoluwa Akintola (9)	123
Eshal Moosa (10)	124
Chiara Dawson (10)	125
Julian Rezwan (9)	126
Olivia Rataj (10)	127
Naomi Sloan (9)	128
Fred Hollis (10)	129
George Duncan (10)	130
Alexander Mackenzie (10)	132
Andrew Hendry (10)	133
Louis Chin Lawrie (10)	134
Thomas Rees (10)	135
Neil Rasalam (10)	136
Oscar Jones (10)	137
Daniel Rose (10)	138
Fraser Murphy (10)	140
Kristina Krsmanovic (10)	141
Harriet Love (10)	142
Esme Rogers (10)	143
Elizabeth Webster (10)	144
Hannah Cowie (10)	145

THE POEMS

How To Make Eva!

Start by adding some intelligence
Next, add some swimming skills
After that, add lots of love for dogs
Once you have done that, mix some energy
And add some sugar and spice
Place in the oven for ten minutes
Then let me out
Once you're done, add a little niceness
Then add an obsession with Harry Potter
Mix again with a dose of roller coasters
Then boil until bubbles show
Pour into a bowl... now I'll soon be ready
Once you have done that
Add melted chocolate and mix
Pop in the fridge and don't take out until 3rd July
Then sprinkle on top of me and ta-da!

Eva Hanbidge (10)
Camphill Primary School, Ballymena

How To Make Amazing Me!

Start by adding a cup of sugar
To make me sweet and nice

A port of glitter
A pan of daisies
That's what makes me twice

A splash of lemon juice
That makes me bitter
Of course, not all the time

Make sure to mix me up well
And I should be tall and artistic

Add some pretty pink food colouring
To make me pretty colours

Don't forget to add chocolate eyes
And brown hair to me

When I'm finished
I need a dress of icing
Make it chocolate, mixed with strawberry

Give me a ball, shinguards
And a stick to play hockey
I will then be a hockey player

Add some animal obsession
And of course, a dose of Harry Potter

Before you put me in the oven of the room
Add some happiness and sparkle
And ounces of laughter

Mix together well
This is me!

Lucy Steenson (10)
Camphill Primary School, Ballymena

This Is Me Rap

I love sports, football is my favourite
But when you talk about Arsenal
I don't listen to it
I really like F1
To watch it is fun
I also like basketball
Although I'm not very tall

I'm a great reader
I really like Harry Potter
Draco from Slytherin, I really like him
Going back to football
I support Chelsea
And Billy Gilmour
Is my favourite player

My favourite foods are
Jambons, chocolate puds
Crisps, chocolate cakes
Sweet and traybakes
That's all until the rest
Because Esther is the best!

Esther Moore (9)
Camphill Primary School, Ballymena

How To Make Brooke

First, get the batter and mould her body
Then make her dislike tomatoes
Next, give her a super hard-working brain
Make sure to give her brown eyes
Add ginger hair and freckles as well
Add to her brain, some cleverness
Make her kind and a comprehension hater
Next, add a tablespoon of sunshine and sea
Then place her in LA or Hawaii
Make her some cookies, give her a cat
And there you have made who everyone calls...
Brooke Eddie!

Brooke Eddie (9)
Camphill Primary School, Ballymena

This Is Me

I have two cats, they're my favourite things
And when they roll around, they're funny
little things
Their names are Mimi and Twinkle, they're the
best cats ever
They will snuggle me whenever
My favourite thing to touch is fur
I could lie on it all day long
My favourite colour is pink
Especially when I have a pink bubblegum drink
This is me, Ruby.

Ruby Corry (10)
Camphill Primary School, Ballymena

How To Make Me!

Throw blue eyes
Into a cauldron

Strand by strand
Add blonde hair

Mix well

Slowly add
Stones from Paris

Stir in Scottish heirlooms

Still mixing
Put in some ballet and jazz

Add a lot of
Victoria sponge cake, yum

A sprinkle of fun
Kindness and noise

And you have me
Charlotte!

Charlotte Baillie (9)
Camphill Primary School, Ballymena

This Is Me Rap!

I go to gymnastics and ju-jitsu
Sporty, crazy, funny, I'd like to say
Don't like chocolate or fizzy drinks
But backflips is my jam and I'd like to say
My birthday's in November and it's autumn
now, yay
My favourite colour's pink and pasta is so nice
I go to Camphill Primary School
It makes me feel like I'm at home.

Jessica Redmond (9)
Camphill Primary School, Ballymena

This Is All About Me, Emily

T alented
H amster wanter
I magination runs wild
S hopping lover

I nfectious laughter
S mile giver

M ile runner
E ntertainer

E xcellent at art
M idnight feaster
I ce skating master
L earning to play piano
Y ounger sibling.

Emily Hill (9)
Camphill Primary School, Ballymena

This Is Me

T all
H ealthy
I ndependent
S killed footballer

I nterested in history
S andy-coloured hair

M athematician
E ntertainer

E xcited for birthdays
T alented goalkeeper
H andsome
A thletic
N eighbourly person.

Ethan Todd (9)
Camphill Primary School, Ballymena

All About Me

A kennings poem

Spider hater
Books rule
Books lover
Swimming lover
Flamingo hater
Roblox player
Best friends
Rugby hater
Cat owner
Dog lover
Hamster lover
New York admirer
Panda lover
Fish lover
Hamsters rule
Paint lover
Guinea pig lover
Winter lover
Spring liker
This is me, Evelyn.

Evelyn Janek (10)
Camphill Primary School, Ballymena

This Is Me

I love to play football and race motocross too
Chocolate is my favourite food
I'm kind, caring and funny, that's what makes me, me
I love to go to Spain and also London for the football matches
I love summer but not the wasps
I have blonde hair and bright blue eyes
Who am I?
I am Alfie.

Alfie Leacock (9)
Camphill Primary School, Ballymena

This Is Me

I love hamsters
And my dogs
I want to go to Lanzarote
My hobby is playing with my hamster
I'm nice, funny, beautiful and a food lover
I don't like guinea pigs, but I love hamsters
I'm brunette, long-haired and a TikToker
I love McDonald's and carbonara
This is me.

Danielle Drummond (9)
Camphill Primary School, Ballymena

All About Me

A kennings poem

Football liker
Spider disliker
Cookie eater
McDonald's lover
Cheese hater
Late sleeper
Early riser
Music fan
Fast reader
Pencil writer
Numeracy expert
Literacy detester
Dog owner
Blue eyes
Tommy Cochrane
This is me.

Tommy Cochrane (9)
Camphill Primary School, Ballymena

This Is Me

A kennings poem

Easily annoyed
Food cruncher
Literacy loather
Lightning fast
Speedy swimmer
Inside stayer
Schoolbag stuffer
Lunch lover
Computer expert
Oldest child
Dividing master
Who am I?

I am Jack.

Jack Moore (10)
Camphill Primary School, Ballymena

This Is Me

A kennings poem

Game lover
Manchester supporter
Carbonara eater
Turtle owner
Blue eyes
Pizza eater
Troublemaker
Football player
Blonde hair
Chicken eater
Book reader
Chicken owner
This is me, Callum.

Callum Kernohan (9)
Camphill Primary School, Ballymena

All About Me

A kennings poem

Hamster lover
Vegetable hater
Meat eater
Pet owner
Portugal traveller
Swimming pool goer
Shark admirer
Guitar player
Action figure player
History studier
Book reader
This is me, Kalel.

Kalel Nelson (10)

Camphill Primary School, Ballymena

This Is Me

A kennings poem

Dog lover
Pizza eater
iPad watcher
Phone player
Literacy lover
Spider hater
Maths liker
Ice cream licker
Roblox player
Lucozade drinker
Crisp muncher
This is me, Holly.

Holly Clarke (10)
Camphill Primary School, Ballymena

This Is Me

My favourite food is burgers
The sport I love is football
I love dogs
I hate spiders
England is my favourite holiday destination
The game I love to play is FIFA
This is me, Corey.

Corey Rainey (9)
Camphill Primary School, Ballymena

This Is Me

A kennings poem

HP lover
Vegetable loather
Brown hair
Blue eyes
Pizza eater
Animal enthusiast
Art admirer
Irish dancer
Spider obsessor
Book reader
This is me, Clare.

Clare Foster (10)
Camphill Primary School, Ballymena

This Is Me

A kennings poem

Rugby player
Meat lover
Pizza lover
PlayStation player
Alex Rider reader
Movie lover
Puppy owner
Instrument player
This is me, Andrew.

Andrew Gardiner (9)
Camphill Primary School, Ballymena

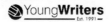

This Is Me, Jude

A kennings poem

Football lover
Spider liker
Chinese eater
Blue lover
Brown disliker
Caramel chocolate lover
Liverpool supporter
This is me, Jude.

Jude Ayre (9)
Camphill Primary School, Ballymena

This Is Me

A kennings poem

Blonde hair
Blue eyes
Homemade chips lover
Vegetable loather
Colouring lover
Portrush goer
Kindness giver
This is me, Miley.

Miley Mcgall (9)
Camphill Primary School, Ballymena

All About Me!

A kennings poem

Football lover
Wasp hater
Mint disliker
Ice cream eater
Lemon liker
Coke drinker
Dog owner
Cat lover
This is me, Owen.

Owen Mairs (10)
Camphill Primary School, Ballymena

This Is Me

A kennings poem

Broccoli loather
Football player
FIFA lover
France admirer
Noodle headed
Meatball eater
Cat owner
This is me.

Ben James (9)
Camphill Primary School, Ballymena

This Is Me

A kennings poem

Dog lover
Hockey player
Apple hater
Disco dancer
Quiet girl
Only child
Glasses wearer
This is me.

Kiona Wylie (9)
Camphill Primary School, Ballymena

All About Me

A kennings poem

Dog lover
Spider detester
Vegetable hater
Hamster admirer
Holiday lover
Rat hater
This is me, Lola.

Lola Ward (9)
Camphill Primary School, Ballymena

This Is Me, Rebecca

A kennings poem

Dog lover
Spider hater
Pizza lover
Potato wedges hater
Panda lover
Cat hater
This is me, Rebecca.

Rebecca Harris (9)
Camphill Primary School, Ballymena

If You Feel This Way

If you ever feel lonely, it's okay
Because people get it, it's okay

If you ever feel sad just think
Of the worst thing that could happen

If you ever feel hurt just
Tell a grown-up
Everything will be okay

Now you know what to do if you feel this way
If you get these feelings, just calm down
And take a moment or two
So now you know what to do.

Aoife Brown (8)
Chapel Road Primary School, Waterside

This Is Me, Sienna

I love art
I hate sprouts
I am silly
I love reading
I hate the cold
I love McDonald's
I hate schoolwork
I am a big sister
I love KFC
I hate fruit
I love Coke
I hate veg
I love sports
I love dogs and bunnies
I am friendly and happy
I love Pepsi, books and skipping
I have fun with my friends and family.
This is me!

Sienna Mcbride (8)
Chapel Road Primary School, Waterside

This Is Me!

I am Kate
From a family of four
I have a dog also
So that's one more

I love gymnastics
Arts and crafts
Too much TV
And I love my baths

I go to Chapel Road Primary
The best school of all
It's here all my friends are
And that's all.

Kate Warne (8)
Chapel Road Primary School, Waterside

This Is All About Me

My brain works like a human calculator
I climb on trees like a monkey
I always play Mario Kart on my phone
I love maths, that's why I always have
something to do
I want to be a football player
I always train for football by my house.

Antoni Keczmerski (8)
Chapel Road Primary School, Waterside

This Is Me!

This is me
I can be who I really want to be
I don't want to be alone
I don't want everyone to moan or groan
This is me, I am not alone
And I don't moan or groan
No one is alone.

Mela McMonagle (8)
Chapel Road Primary School, Waterside

Everything I Love

I love KFC as well as peas
My mummy helps with the cooking
I love Minecraft 1.18, educating too
Gaelic is fun
But I'm more Slaughtmanus
My mummy helps me a lot
So I help her!

Rose Ward (8)
Chapel Road Primary School, Waterside

Like And Dislike

I think I'm good at football
Maybe I am wrong
I really hate singing songs
I loved going to Spain
I hate feeling pain
I like drinking Coke
I don't like when I boke.

Lennon McDermott (9)
Chapel Road Primary School, Waterside

I Love Monkeys But Hate Bananas

I would really love a monkey
But sometimes it might be cheeky
And they really love bananas
But I'd rather walk to Africa
From Australia than eat a banana.

Devin Obinna (9)
Chapel Road Primary School, Waterside

This Is Me

Harry Potter, he is so strong
I'm being him for Halloween
I love the books
The second book is scary
I love it so much, it is fun.

Daniel Devine (9)
Chapel Road Primary School, Waterside

Me

Amaya Patel is a monkey
All day long she is jumpy
Music is her favourite hobby
She likes to move with her body
She loves to eat lots of food
And play around in a good mood
You know, Amaya is a dancing monkey
She likes her chips rather chunky
Amaya's hair is big and silky
And she likes her Weetabix milky.

Amaya Patel (7)
Hydesville Tower School, Walsall

Happiness To Me

H orse riding and pony club
A rtistic and creative fun
P laying outside in the sun
P iano and flute
I ncredible tasting ice creams
N ewly found adventures in my dreams
E njoyable family time
S uch important things
S uper sweet happiness brings.

Avaani Khera (8)
Hydesville Tower School, Walsall

Connections

Who are they?
They help me when I am sad
They always calm me down when I'm mad
I always see them by my side
I know they're there because when I cry
They're always being kind to me
So I shall try to be kind to them
Who are they?

They are family and friends.

Ruby Raiye (8)
Hydesville Tower School, Walsall

This Is Me

Y uvraj is my name
U nder my silliness, I'm caring
V ery confident in subjects
R attling snakes are my favourite animal
A nd I am a jaguar when I'm racing
J umping on my trampoline like a kangaroo is fun.

Yuvraj Gurbax Singh Sunner (8)

Hydesville Tower School, Walsall

This Is Me

Hi! I'm a girl and my name is Evie,
And I'm smart since I find learning easy.
I do like football even though I'm a girl,
A bit of a tomboy, I hate to twirl.

Hi! I love archaeology when it's bright
But I'm scared of the dark, especially at night.
No, photography's the best,
Loads better than rugby where you get no rest.

Hello too!
Sorry it's my brother, let's learn about you.
My three best friends are Slytherin, Hufflepuff and
Ravenclaw,
We're big Harry Potter dorks.

Salute! My favourite place is France,
Though I live in the UK, I still love to prance.
I do hate ducks, I'm terrified of ducks,
I'd just love to go pluck, pluck, pluck!

Hi again! Gaming all day is the best,
I also love visitors or guests.
I love dinos and dragons,
Oh they were the cutest by galleons!

I like lots of things which are unique,
I'm also the same but still so sleek.
I can be bright, as bright as the moon,
Plus I'll see you soon!

Evie Barter (10)
Northleigh CE Primary School, Malvern

My Favourite Animal

My favourite animal is full to the brim with fur,
He loves to purr,
Some could say as slow as a sloth,
He will always roll around in the table cloth,
He's always going to land on his feet,
But won't sleep very neat,
He is the king of a kip,
And goes crazy on catnip,
A swishing tail, firm and strong,
Sadly, he's not so strong,
In the streets he's royalty,
Sometimes he's silly just like me,
He has the sharpest claws,
But you will never see them as they are hidden in his paws,
He is the best,
But makes a bit of a mess,
He loves stealing food,
When you touch him on the belly it puts him in a mood,

He loves watching the world go by,
Looking at his face, he might lie,
Also,
This animal is pretty heavy,
And his name is Freddie...

Fraser Rusling
Northleigh CE Primary School, Malvern

My Autistic Mind

E veryone knows I love to write stories
V ideo gaming is one of my hobbies
A n author is what I dream of becoming

R ats and dogs are two of my favourite animals
O n my birthday, I feel as special as an emerald
S pending time with my family gives me a fantastic feeling
E ven when I'm feeling sad, I can always walk away

G reat big ideas fill my imagination
R eally beautiful music makes me want to sing and dance
E very day, I'm as busy as a bee
E xtra special superpowers
N ever leave my brain.

Eva Green (7)
Northleigh CE Primary School, Malvern

A Narrative Poem

My name is Rohan or Ron for short.
I'm small like a mouse but wise like an elephant.
I have two dogs and seven fish.
I'm a follower and a leader of the pack
My favourite animal is a wolf, well canine really.
I laugh like a hyena and sometimes a duck.
I'm not trying to be funny, so if you meet me don't look at me funny.
I've got a few annoying habits, well who doesn't really.
Here's a few more facts about me.
My favourite actor is Samuel L Jackson.
I like the movie series Avengers.
I'm a gamer but prefer to hang with my dogs.
I love my family.
Well now folks, that's me, bye.

Rohan Doyle
Northleigh CE Primary School, Malvern

My Favourite Animal

A reptile that slithers through the mangroves and forests,
A beast, who hunts larger animals than itself.
It sometimes eats sheep, cats, dogs and even goats,
They open their neck flaps aggressively when something is agitating them.
If you see one stay calm because its deadly poison can ruin the fun game of life,
Their tongues are shockingly scarier than on a TV, their mouths are deep, dark caves with pools of slimy acid.
The saggy acid glands look like a human stomach,
The razor-sharp teeth stick out like daggers,
They are the pointy spikes Venom dons with his symbiotic suit.

Thomas Davies (11)
Northleigh CE Primary School, Malvern

Crazy Me, Yes Crazy Me!

I want a pet but my mum says not yet
I am crazy and sometimes lazy
But I don't care because I've got blonde hair
I am sometimes greedy and very speedy
I can't ride a bike but at least there's no fight
My name is Hetty but people call me spaghetti
I like school, even though it sometimes feels
like a mall

I am cool but people say I'm tall
I like myself even if I don't have the greatest health
I like dance even if I get in a prance
I like being me.

Hetty Pinder (7)
Northleigh CE Primary School, Malvern

All About Me

I am as fast as lightning
I am as sneaky as a prowling tiger
I like trickling streams going through a wood
I like dogs and animals
I like friendship and family
I'm not good at riding
But that doesn't stop me trying
I'm adventurous and playful
But sometimes painful
I like sport with my friends
Sometimes theirs ends
I like Greek gods
I like myths but only Greek ones
I like monsters and Zeus, the god of lightning
I'd like to fly until I die.

Daniel Philpotts (7)
Northleigh CE Primary School, Malvern

What Is It?

A clambering creature that leaps through trees
And sometimes has a peep over leaves.
A leader of balance; lively and strong
A wiggling tail fluffy and long.
Eating bananas day by day,
Up in the trees the furry mammal lay.
These animals live in the jungle
And the creatures never seem to stumble.
They munch on their favourite fruits,
In their canopy high above all the roots.
This animal will always be a ninja of the treetops.
What is it?

Answer: A monkey!

Frankie Moore (11)
Northleigh CE Primary School, Malvern

My World, So Beautiful

My world is beautiful with red roses.
I like chocolate and the world as much as you.
Water as sparkly as the sea so blue,
Dogs so barky.

My world is so beautiful.
I like the world, but you need to pick up litter.
It's hurting all the animals in the world.
Like whales and birds and fish, dolphins and
others.

I love red roses and water and butterflies.
So do you, so look after the world and others.

Isla Grace Smith (7)
Northleigh CE Primary School, Malvern

What Is The Animal?

A courageous creature not too fussy
Sometimes they can be a bit mussy
Not too short not too tall
But their little babies are quite small
They eat fruit and veg for their daytime meal
I don't know how they talk but they could squeal
Their pride is all that matters
They will definitely know how to climb ladders
They pass over the world as they bounce
When they first were discovered there was a big
announce.

Answer: A kangaroo.

Alexis Evans (10)
Northleigh CE Primary School, Malvern

This Is Me

This is me
I am like a deep pool just waiting for someone to
jump in
I am a for sale house just wishing someone will buy
me soon
I am as tired as a parent even though I have no
kids
I am as sassy as a person from a fashion runway
I am as equal as a maths problem for hating
plastic pollution and water slides
I am like a crazy cat that has a dog and a family
and I love them both
This is me!

Holly Thomson (9)
Northleigh CE Primary School, Malvern

What Is It?

A silly creature that swings,
Like silly string on a sunny day.
A master balancer straight and
Strong, jiggly tail furry and long.
They love bananas and they are
Very sneaky.
They are very cheeky when they feast.
They are tall as a toddler they
Make silly sounds they eat bananas and
Lie in their homes fast asleep.
What is it?

Answer: A monkey.

Paige Bessesen (10)
Northleigh CE Primary School, Malvern

This Is Me

I am a dog bed for any golden retriever
I am a double cheeseburger waiting to be eaten
I am a defensive defender on the backline
I am a football being booted up the pitch
I am a guitar pick waiting to be struck
I am a blank canvas waiting to be drawn on
I am a plant getting rained on from above
I am a skateboard rolling on the pavement
This is me!

Jessie Wood (9)
Northleigh CE Primary School, Malvern

This Is Me!

I am a Lego brick, making models galore,
I am a supersonic laugh so I never ever snore.
I am physically a game controller, pressing buttons at speed,
I am like an unstoppable bot, when I'm climbing trees.
My dog is like a security guard,
Barking here and there.
Cross-country running through the streets,
And I love that sweet fresh air.
This is me!

Oliver Dyson (10)
Northleigh CE Primary School, Malvern

This Is Me!

T he sight of my blue-green eyes is unusual

H ave a YouTube channel

I ts link is on Google

S till play Minecraft for an hour (probably way more)

I love my family friends and more

S till on my PC, how do I not get bored?

M eet my dog my hamster my fish too!

E ating my pizza? How dare you!

Amelie Barker (9)
Northleigh CE Primary School, Malvern

What Animal Is It?

Cries with no mother, but laughs with a brother.
If it gets mad you might be sad.
When it's on a branch it does not stumble,
However, if the branch is loose it might cause a
rumble.
Eating bananas is a favourite for them and their
tummy
Maybe that's why they're so grumpy
They never get bananas
What animal is it?

Answer: A spider monkey.

Szymon Olszewski (11)
Northleigh CE Primary School, Malvern

I Love My Family

This is me
I love skateboarding
It's my favourite thing to do
I love my cat called Milly
She lies on my bed for the night
I love my sister called Evie-May
I love my mum and dad as much as my sister
I love my teddy called Pipin, he's a dog
I am playing with my laptop and iPhone
I love watching YouTube
I am a pet lover as well.

Lydia Brown (7)
Northleigh CE Primary School, Malvern

What Animal Is It?

The leader of the jungle that likes to swing,
Swinging all day is its favourite thing,
A master of balance straight and strong,
Their majestic tails are thick and long,
High up in the trees they like to stay,
In the canopy they like to lay,
A human-like creature, oh so sweet,
The type of animal you'd like to meet.
What is it?

Answer: A monkey.

Ruby Mullen (11)
Northleigh CE Primary School, Malvern

This Is Me

I am a super striker
I am a fantastic finisher
I am so quick my wheels fall off
Sometimes I am just a blur
Batting or bowling I am good at both
My best friend has a tail and rips my homework
I am like my family's dustbin for food
Screaming as I win online
I am as happy as a boy in a sweet shop with school
This is me!

Luca Drinkwater (9)
Northleigh CE Primary School, Malvern

This Is Me!

I'm a need-to-know-it-all from around the world
I'm a dog lover, chasing my dog Parker up and
down the field *Zooooooooooooooooooom*
I'm a proud girl even though I broke my arm I'm
still going to gymnastics
I'm a silly, funny person all the time
I'm a pizza, burger, sweet lover, I go bananas over
it
This is me!

Eloise Ireson (10)
Northleigh CE Primary School, Malvern

A Rhyming Poem About Me

This is me,
I'm a basketball player,
A baseball hater,
An amazing dribbler,
A terrible bat swinger,
Faster than a zebra,
But slower than a cheetah,

As quiet as a mouse,
And as still as a house,
I am very calming,
But I can be quite maddening,
Gentle like a honey bee,
Usually a me not we,
I've got knotty 4b hair,
And I'm picky what to wear.
This is me.

Rihanna Vera Cruz (10)
Northleigh CE Primary School, Malvern

What Am I?

A spritely creature full of fun,
Who likes to play in the sun,
Master of the trees,
Who also carries fleas,
A graceful creature; regal and tall,
Have a crazy sort of call,
Eating bananas day by day,
In the canopy where they stay,
If you come too close,
I'll nick your clothes,
I am like a thief,
I'll pocket it like a leaf.
What am I?

Emmeline Illston (11)
Northleigh CE Primary School, Malvern

This Is Me!

T he Earth is where I live

H ate snakes

I love puppies and pandas

S isters and my mum are who I love the most

I dislike ice cream

S illy me, I forgot my dad

M e is who I am and I don't want to change me

E specially my friends too.

Lois Cox (9)

Northleigh CE Primary School, Malvern

This Is Me

I am caring for dogs
I am glued to my iPad Air
I am a water baby
I like to be stuck on to my Xbox
Football cuts through my family
I am a fantastic dog walker
I love to go on a walk with my dad at night
I am a bin lorry for doughnuts
I am as friendly as a nice policeman
This is me.

Hayden Golder (9)
Northleigh CE Primary School, Malvern

What Am I?

A human-like creature that swings like a king,
Swinging on branches it's my favourite thing,
A swishing tail furry and long,
A master of balance; straight and strong
Going round doing crazy things all night long,
I love bananas, it's a thing,
I worship it like a king.
What am I?

Answer: A monkey.

Evie-May Brown (10)
Northleigh CE Primary School, Malvern

This Is Me

I am a drawing doodler drawing as fast as a cheetah
I am a bourbon eater my tongue tingling for sugar
My eyes read books like an Olympian sprinting for the finish
My head is happier than a gold medal-winning champion
My friends are even more amazing than a house made of diamond
This is me!

Ellen Johnson (9)
Northleigh CE Primary School, Malvern

Amazing Alex

B roken both arms
I nventor is my future's job
T en years old, as old as a decade

O tters are my animal of preference
F orgetter of importance, rememberer of facts

M y science I love, it is so good
E verlasting laughter.

Alex Pedlar (10)
Northleigh CE Primary School, Malvern

This Is Me

T errible at handstands
H ates pickles and olives
I nsane at Nerf wars
S illy

I love birds and dogs
S ometimes kisses my pets except my fish

M arshmallow lover
E ats chips, burgers and pizza sometimes.

Sonny Collins (9)

Northleigh CE Primary School, Malvern

This Is Me

I am a master of friendship
I am a songwriter
My eyes are as blue as the ocean
I'm the best singer in my street
I love movies
I love puppies and dogs
I love watermelon
I love reading
I love poems
I love school
I love my family
This is me.

Kate-Lynn Doyle (7)
Northleigh CE Primary School, Malvern

This Is Me

T iny I am
H elpful and friendly
I like animals especially cats
S illy and confident

I like food
S even siblings I have

M e I am bossy
E ven though I'm wacky in a way I'm happy to be me.

Isabell Kyle (9)

Northleigh CE Primary School, Malvern

This Is Me

Mischievous is what people know me for
I am so kind that it flows through my blood
If I have too much fruit I will turn into a fruit tree
When I see a spider it's like it has frozen me in time
The pastel colours flow into my heart every time I
smile
This is me.

Thillali Boussaid (9)
Northleigh CE Primary School, Malvern

This Is Me

I am words flying out of my pencil
I am like a striker in the Champions League
I am like a fish in water
I eat like a monster eater
I am higher than you think from the moon
I am a fantastic helper with my best friend
I am like a monster dominating the game.

Riley Virgo (9)

Northleigh CE Primary School, Malvern

My Favourite Animal

I am scaly and deadly,
My venom can kill you,
I'm not very friendly,
I have no ears,
I sense with my tongue,
My big brother can eat deer,
My friends are straight and strong,
We have thin tails that are long,
I have big fangs that can pierce your skin,
My body is thin.
What am I?

Archie Tyler (10)
Northleigh CE Primary School, Malvern

This Is Me

M y life is football and family

A mazing at maths

T all and talented

T errified of needles

H orrified of watching myself

E verybody is nice in my class

W ell I love everything I have and I am thankful for it.

Matthew Hale (10)

Northleigh CE Primary School, Malvern

This Is Me!

I am as small as a kingfisher diving down low
I am as pleasant as a Pegasus soaring above the clouds
I am as worried as an animal that's lost their home
I am as bright as the countryside is big
I am as soft as my cat that curls up so small
This is me.

Anusha Jackson (9)
Northleigh CE Primary School, Malvern

This Is Me

I am as stretchy as a rubber band
I am a human vacuum for any food
My lungs are a radio machine
My hair is as crazy as you

I am as sweet as a sweet
My eyes are a magnet to a screen
My home is where I'm next to my cat
This is me.

Tabitha Forde (9)
Northleigh CE Primary School, Malvern

This Is Me

This is me,
I am a lover of my adorable dog
I am like a cupcake with lots of frosting
I am like the ocean waiting for the plastic to be
removed
I am like a mini Albert Einstein
I am like a hot glue gun as I glue the family
together
This is me!

Farah Eccleston (9)
Northleigh CE Primary School, Malvern

This Is Me

I'm a pixelated fighter searching for loot
I am like a Minecraft Steve building a mansion
I'm a walking talking paintbrush
I am a mouse searching for pizza instead of cheese
I'm a kicking killer finding footballs to kick
That was me!

Ryan Philpotts (10)
Northleigh CE Primary School, Malvern

Me

I am a gaming addict.
I am a homework hater.
I am a food lover.
I am a movie watcher.
I am a car-naming master.
I am a math genius.
I am a god at being annoying.
I am brilliant at waking up at 6am.
I am amazing at hide-and-seek.
I am good at long-distance throwing.

Danniel Choudhury (10)
Northleigh CE Primary School, Malvern

What Animal Is It?

A cute cuddly creature
That thinks and swings in the dark brown trees,
They lie in the night and when it is bright
They take berries off the rustling leaves,
No harm will be done when this little creature has fun
In the warmth of the hot glowing sun.

Zeva B-H
Northleigh CE Primary School, Malvern

This Is Me

I am a racing roller coaster seeking fun
I am like a sewing machine hungry for fabric
My taste buds are tingling for sugary sweetness
My body is like an elastic band
My head of hair in the morning is crazier than a
wacky party
This is me!

Edie Pinder (9)
Northleigh CE Primary School, Malvern

This Is Me!

I am a happy friend playing
I am a singing star with a voice like a bird
I am a cake eater that loves chocolate
I am a cute dog lover that likes fluffy ones
I am a dancing angel that leaps gracefully
I am a sky-eyed unicorn
This is me!

Kaycie Evans (9)
Northleigh CE Primary School, Malvern

This Is Me

I am as graceful as a fish swimming in the ocean
I am a crazy fan of cats
I am a chocolate bar ready to be vanished
I am an imaginary person ready for someone to hug me
I am a happy smiley face when playing with my friends.
This is me.

Phoebe Wiggett (9)
Northleigh CE Primary School, Malvern

My Favourite Animal

It's a furry friend,
One you can cuddle,
He'll purr when you stroke him,
He'll scratch when you play with him,
He's energetic and fast,
But old and lazy,
They come in all sorts of shapes and sizes,
And a few different colours.
What is it?

Ben Rusling
Northleigh CE Primary School, Malvern

This Is Me!

I am an F1 driver speeding at 200mph through the apex of Silverstone
I am a happiness monkey with my friends beside me
I am a speeding king when I am riding my motorbike
I am a pizza praiser
I am a sleeper monster
This is me!

Benjamin Powles (10)

Northleigh CE Primary School, Malvern

This Is Me!

I am an F1 driver on the straights of Silverstone
I am an Xbox gamer
I am like the sky with my blinding blue eyes
I am like a Ferrari driver when it comes to sports day
I am a flying food eater when I'm hungry
This is me!

Samuel Cutts (10)

Northleigh CE Primary School, Malvern

Animal Riddle

A human-like creature that swings like a king.
A king of balance with a long strong tail.
Consuming berries day by day,
As I play in my very unique way.
Lying high in the brown trees I lie.
I'm big and strong,
But...
What am I?

Kaiden Pearce (10)
Northleigh CE Primary School, Malvern

This Is Me

I am a rag toy for any German shepherd
I am a policeman with the sirens wailing
I am a blank canvas waiting to be painted
I am a coin dropping into the hands of the poor
I am a plant waiting to be watered
This is me.

Richie Smith (9)

Northleigh CE Primary School, Malvern

This Is Me!

I am a football drawn to the goals
I am a meal for sad souls
I am a pencil made to go on paper
I am a water surfboard saver
I am a body ready to share
I am imagination that always cares

This is me!

Poppy Whakahau (9)
Northleigh CE Primary School, Malvern

This Is Me!

I am a fish finder round the lake I catch,
My family is a perfect match,
When I play rugby I always score tries,
When people leave my house I always say my byes,
This is Alfie he never tells lies,
This is me!

Alfie Tedds (9)
Northleigh CE Primary School, Malvern

What Is It?

A crazy master of the day
Consuming berries to keep at bay
This man-like creature king of the jungle
When they fight it's a bit of a rumble
When in the trees they never stumble
Down the hill it's a bit of a tumble.

Thomas Summerfield (10)
Northleigh CE Primary School, Malvern

This Is Me

A kennings poem

I am a...

Military daughter
Youngest sibling
A deep sleeper
Sweet lover
Caring sister
Crazy person
Good boxer
Tea lover
And finally...
A good friend.

Faith (9)
Northleigh CE Primary School, Malvern

This Is Me

I am a clothes store ranger
I am a human cloth in ballet
I am a mouth-watering doughnut hoover
I am a fast organiser
I am a magic carpet gliding around the world
This is me.

Ellie Mitchell (10)
Northleigh CE Primary School, Malvern

This Is Me

A kennings poem

I am a...
Teddy hugger,
Apple eater,
Rock climber,
Dog stroker,
Cake decorator,
House point counter,
Water drinker,
And finally,
Book reader.

Anna Jones (9)

Northleigh CE Primary School, Malvern

This Is Me

A kennings poem

I am a...
Military daughter
Animal lover
Horse rider
Light sleeper
Early riser
Crazy daughter
Game player
And finally...
A good friend.

Harriet Perkins (9)
Northleigh CE Primary School, Malvern

This Is Me

This is me
I am neat
I won't take others' opinions
Because I am me
I want to be a doctor
Help people in need
With a lovely attitude
So they can succeed
I believe in a motto
Very simple it is indeed
I call it BAS, it stands for
Believe, achieve, succeed
I love my school
It taught me this motto
Yes, it did indeed
I want the best for others
Just like my mother wants for me
I wish for the world to have happiness
And for nastiness to go away
Love all around
Together we can save the day.

Addison Flewin (9)
Pomphlett Primary School, Plymstock

A Perfect Pomphlett Pupil

I am Harriet Abbott and I am nine years old
I'm tall and blonde and do as I'm told
I play lots of rugby which makes me happy
Often I come home very mucky
I live in Sherford with my family
This includes my little brother, Leo and sister, Ezzy
I love my bicycle and cycle to the park
Sometimes I get home and it's very dark
My favourite subject in school is maths
And Miss Shaw gives us lots of laughs
I really hope you enjoyed learning about me
So I can win the goody bag, hehehe!

Harriet Abbott (9)
Pomphlett Primary School, Plymstock

Me On The Inside!

This is me on the inside
These are my thoughts and wonders
This is me on the inside
Sounding like thunder
This is me on the inside
My head constantly spinning
This is me on the inside
Where my dreams are only just beginning
This is me on the inside
Worried about starting big school
This is me on the inside
Worrying about others being cruel
This is me on the inside
Knowing I will be fine
It's okay to be a storm of emotions
All at the same time.

Maddison Mather (9)
Pomphlett Primary School, Plymstock

I Am Me!

I am kind and generous
I love dancing and reading
I worry about my dog, Hunny, in the sky
I dream about being an author
I love Christmas because my family
celebrate together
I feel calm taking walks in the woods
I believe in mythical creatures
I am Willow
I am me.

Willow Gordon (7)
Pomphlett Primary School, Plymstock

Me And My Poem

S unshine glows in the sky

T each the class

E aster eggs are very delicious

V iolet is a beautiful colour

I ce is cold

E xcited to go horse riding.

Stevie Hopkin (10)
Pomphlett Primary School, Plymstock

Chloe

C hloe is my name
H ow about a lazy day?
L ove is something everyone needs
O bviously, I love to be weird
E ating is a hobby of mine.

Chloe Kelly (10)
Pomphlett Primary School, Plymstock

This Is Me

I have blonde hair like sand on a beach
My eyes are blue like the ocean and the sea
I have three pets, they are the best
When I'm on my bike, I speed like the wind
I have a brother and a mum and dad
I love reading and cuddling my cat
He is the best cat in the whole wide world
So, if I were an animal, I would definitely be a cat
I love kayaking in the lakes and lochs
My dad usually rows
I love pizza and popcorn
They are really good and my favourite food
I love animals, almost all of them
I think spiders are creepy, I don't like them at all
They are way too creepy for me
At school, I love PE and sports and swimming
I am excellent at maths and I love it too
My dog's name is Yogi
My cats' names are Freya and Cheeky
This is me!

Antonina Weychan (9)
Robert Gordon's College, Aberdeen

This Is Me

Isla is my name
I am as fast as the wind
When there's a stick in my hand
I love walking on a hot sunny beach with
burning sand
I'm a fence clearer when on a horse
And when falling off I still feel no remorse
I'm as friendly as a puppy but like a lion, I'm strong
I'm not amazing at maths and do get a
couple wrong
If I were a food, I think I'd be a grape
As I'm small and not tall
But colourful and mostly great
I have a competitive mindset
But if someone falls, I'll help them up
And take them the rest of the way
Even if I'm exhausted
I will try my best the whole day
And I'm always careful about what I say
My friends are amazing and definitely the best

However, my adorable, chubby brother is
quite the pest
My eyes are as green as a leaf
With hair the colour of a caramel chocolate bar
I love doing art with a long pencil
The colour of the blackest black tar
This is me!

Isla Clark (10)

Robert Gordon's College, Aberdeen

This Is Me

This me, Kosi with a K
Not cosy with a C
I'm not as warm as you can see
My favourite colour is blue
there is a lot that I can do
I always try my very best
Sometimes my brother can be a pest
I'm like blue fire when it comes to basketball
I'm always kind to all
I'm like Zeus' lightning bolt
When it comes to Greek gods and goddesses
I'm like the king of the jungle
Because I can take control when I need to
I'm like a grey cloud
Because I bottle up my emotions
I always try to be very happy
Even though I can get quite angry
I have good friends that don't make me cry
And make me happier than seeing a cute dog
Chow Chow puppies are my favourite type of dogs
I hope I end up getting one, one day

I also like cats but they are not my favourite
As I like dogs more
Cats run away and hide from their owners
That's it all about me, Kosi with a K
And not cosy with a C.

Kosi Ileagu (10)
Robert Gordon's College, Aberdeen

This Is Me

If I were an animal, I would be...
The king of the ocean
The top of the food chain
The bullet in the sea
If I was a food, I would be...
A planet on a stick on the top
Cut into quarters and eaten whole
Rolling away ready to be collected
If I were an object, I would be...
The top toy of the field
Bought, stopped, kicked or played
With many capabilities
Like scoring goals or being saved
Big and round, in different colours
Lying proudly on the grass
If I were a colour, I would be...
The colour of the deep ocean
Or the colour of the clear beautiful sky
Or the colour of the clear, transparent raindrops
Proudly near the bottom of the rainbow
Going from dark to light

Proudly the colour of the Scottish flag
And sparkling sapphire
A colour of which is unique in all its ways
This is me, Charles.

Charles Leroy (10)
Robert Gordon's College, Aberdeen

This Is Me!

I am as fast as a bullet when I am racing to
the finish
I feel like a bird when I fly off the big ramps
Skiing is my favourite sport and I never want
to stop

I am very lucky with my family, well, my mum and
dad are great
But my sister, on the other hand, does something
I hate
She burst into my room and messes with my toys
She sounds like a monster when she's making that
big noise
But I still love her anyway and I think she loves
me back

I am small but not tall and I am fine with that
I have the appearance of a beach
With my sandy blonde hair and my sea-blue eyes
My spelling isn't great and I have tried to be
resilient to this very date

I am Andrew and I'm proud of that
I am Andrew and this is me.

Andrew Hendrie (10)

Robert Gordon's College, Aberdeen

If I Were An Animal, I Would Be...

I'm very cunning and strong
Very fast and very long
I'm intelligent and smart
And always want to look the part

I love travelling and school
Comprehension is just not cool
A torpedo in the water
In competitions, I will slaughter

I'm alert and sporty
And mostly very happy
I am fit and healthy
I hunt food very stealthily

My piano and chanter
Will make other animals scamper
As the loud noise booms
Deafening creatures in the gloom

I'm as long as a kite
I will win in a fight
And no one knew that a deadly snake
Was hunting in the night

So if I were an animal
I would be a snake
My personality matches with it
And a match like that I'll take.

Ryan Knox (9)
Robert Gordon's College, Aberdeen

This Is Me

I am sporty
I am kind
I am helpful
I am friendly
This is me
I am competitive
I am funny
And football is my hobby
This is me
My strong point is maths
But I despise comprehension
I'm as sleepy as a sloth
But when it comes to rugby and football
I am very energetic
I love to play video games
My favourite subject is swimming
This is me
I also like drama, sport, PE, maths and art
I play for a football team called Culter F.C.
And I really enjoy it
This is me

I also play the chanter
And I'm nearly on the bagpipes
And finally, my favourite food is sushi
It's amazing
My name is Ryan
I'm ten years old and this is me.

Ryan Lees (10)
Robert Gordon's College, Aberdeen

This Is Me

If I were an animal, I would be...
As quiet as a bat
As sneaky as a snake
Like a monkey in the trees
The ruler of the Amazon rainforest
I would be a jaguar
I like history and science
But RME is just too much for me
If I were a food, I would be...
Anything but dairy
I would be a bit sugary and a bit healthy
I would be the one and only strawberry
My favourite colour is the colour of ice
And diamonds, it is cyan
My hobbies are running in the cold breeze
Having with my brother, it's the best
I hate being left out or getting hurt
If I were the weather, I would be...

The darkest one out there
The holder of lightning
I would be thunder
This is me!

Lucas Baird (10)
Robert Gordon's College, Aberdeen

This Is Me

My name is Lilia
I am always happy
I am never in misery
I can jump like a kangaroo
I am as fast as a turtle too
I will never put pineapple on pizza
I will put mushy, miserable mushrooms from Ibiza
I can be a wasp fleer
I am told I am a book reader
Summer is my favourite holiday
The 7th July is my birthday
I love to prance and play netball
All my friends prefer basketball
I really do love the sea
I also want to save the bees
I am never in a mood
I really love food
I study Japan
Like I am its biggest fan

I am as sweet as a gummy
I can be really funny
This is me.

Lilia Sheed (10)
Robert Gordon's College, Aberdeen

Renée DK

I'm Renée
And I'm just here to say
Some things about me
And also what I want to be

I'm stubborn at times
But I persevere and solve the rhymes
I'm very chatty to my friends
It drives some people round the bend

I'm high-spirited and bold
By the way, I am nine years old
I like playing with my puppy, he brings me joy
He has a stuffed little elephant, it's his
favourite toy

I want to be a biologist when I leave school
I think it will be really cool
That is the end of my poem, you see
Now you know a bit more about me.

Renée De Kock (9)
Robert Gordon's College, Aberdeen

All About Me

I am an animal lover
Golden retrievers are my thing
I am as adventurous as a panther
Athletics is my everything
My hair is darker than a night without any stars
My eyes are colder than the planet Mars

Making cupcakes makes me smile
Further than two miles
I am the oldest of three
My two little brothers look up to me
I am a kid who cares
Who really fears bears

Endangered species I am keen on
Polar bears really need a shoulder to lean on
I will help when I can
I'm not superhuman
You can't tell me what I can be
Because this is me!

Ireoluwa Akintola (9)
Robert Gordon's College, Aberdeen

This Is Me

I have black hair like the night sky passes
I can see far clearly with my shiny glasses
I'm an ecstatic musician when I play the piano
I'm a messy baker when I bake cookies, my
mum says
I'm a bookworm when I'm reading but as sleepy
as a sloth
Tennis is my passion, energetic as a bee
Swatting the shuttlecock like a fly that's
annoying me
I love biriyani, this spicy makes my day
I hate tomatoes, the nasty tomatoes will pay
I'm intelligent in maths, my fractions are so fast
Off to be a bookworm, just kidding, let's sleep at
last.

Eshal Moosa (10)

Robert Gordon's College, Aberdeen

This Is Me

I am an only child with no pets
I go horse riding and I love seeing the horse, Raven
I would be if I were an animal, a horse or a lion
Because they are very clever

I am a fan of the saying
"An apple a day keeps the doctor away."
So if I were a fruit, I would be an apple
The food that has taken my liking is the
crisp, Wotsit
The drink that I love is cold milk

I am as messy as a puppy
Mum has two and a half sets of parents
So I have loads of uncles
Even though I am Scottish
My name is Italian
I go to school at RGC.

Chiara Dawson (10)
Robert Gordon's College, Aberdeen

This Is Me, Julian Without An E

Chocolate cake
Is something I hate
Some may call me a fool
But I say I'm cool

I'm a kid who cares
And I'm quite picky about my hair
I was born in November
It's the best month ever

My favourite colour is green
And I really hate beans
I love playing with my friends
When I play tig with them
I hope it never ends

I'm the youngest in my family
And that sometimes comes in handy
My mum says I'm a risk-taker
But that's what makes me Julian
Without an 'E'!

Julian Rezwan (9)
Robert Gordon's College, Aberdeen

126

This Is Me

My name is Olivia
I enjoy pineapple on pizza
My favourite colour is sage-green
And I am never mean
If I am in a mood, bring me food
Preferably chicken curry
I'm in a hurry
I'm bold, I'm brave
I love going on holiday
I'm as flexible as an elastic band
I am really sporty and competitive
I get annoyed really
I am as strong as a metal pole
A lot of people know me for my dancing
I am Maui Thai fighter too
My birthday is the 24th of May
I am cool, kind, friendly and awesome
This is me!

Olivia Rataj (10)
Robert Gordon's College, Aberdeen

My Life

M y name is Naomi and this is me, making crafts and being active

Y oung, blonde hair like the sand, blue eyes like the ocean, this is me

L ive the life the life is lived

I am me and my family loves me

F ind the life in me, you will see my smile

E veryone has their own life but I am me and this is me

N ice, kind and friendly, this is me

A cting energetic, this is me

O n time, mostly

M agnificent at talking

I ntelligent at all of these things.

Naomi Sloan (9)

Robert Gordon's College, Aberdeen

This Is Me

I am sporty and competitive
I am strong and brave
I am as fast as
The speed of light in football boots
If I were a food, I would be...
Popcorn... warm, crunchy
And covered in delicious caramel
Oozing all over
Football and rugby are my passions
Getting muddy is a must
Gaming is another favourite
Fortnite and Minecraft everywhere
I like to swim in the sea
And I am as fast as a fish
I have a shot as powerful as a rhino in football
I am very healthy
And love to read books
This is me, Fred.

Fred Hollis (10)
Robert Gordon's College, Aberdeen

This Is Me

My name is George
I do a lot of things
But the main thing that I do
Is eat lots of food

I'm super sporty
And as fast as a cheetah
I make supersonic sound
I score more than Ronaldo

I am a gamer
I love to run and jump
I sweat behind the screen

I love biking
I cycle everywhere
Who needs a car
When you can bike there?

Beautiful Ballater
Is a great place to explore

A fantastic village for family
Friends and more.
This is me.

George Duncan (10)
Robert Gordon's College, Aberdeen

This Is Me

My name is Alexander
I am very energetic
I am very active
I am as fast as a cheetah
I am very fast at climbing
I am in the loud pipe band
I love the amazing weekends
I love my cute pet hamster, Haribo
I love to play lots of rugby
I love to play with my toys
I like to do drumming
I like to play video games
I like my fun friends
I like my parents
I like my caring family
My favourite food is pizza
My favourite animal is a wolf
My favourite friend is Louis
This is me!

Alexander Mackenzie (10)
Robert Gordon's College, Aberdeen

This Is Me

My name is Andrew
Farming is my passion
I couldn't do it without
My lucky Stanley spanner
My family always supports me, no matter what
Working with wood, manufacturing with metal
Or even engines, it really doesn't matter
The roaring of the engines
The scent of the coffee through the house
That's what gets me up at night
The sound of my ratchet
That's what lulls me to sleep at night
When I leave the house I always
Make sure Stanley is in my pocket
This is me!

Andrew Hendry (10)
Robert Gordon's College, Aberdeen

This Is Me

I'm Louis
I love BMXing
I like doing some drumming
I don't like the rain
But I love dumplings
Badminton is my favourite sport
You shouldn't play if you're really short
My hair is really dark
It looks like tree bark
Maths is fun but I don't like to run
I play in the pipe band, it is really loud
It makes me super proud
My favourite colour is red
I love lying in my bed
I am as reactive as lightning
I do judo which is skilled fighting
This is me.

Louis Chin Lawrie (10)
Robert Gordon's College, Aberdeen

This Is Me

If I were an animal, I would be...
A stealthy spider
Never scared to hunt others bigger than me
Do not put me in the water, I can't swim very well
I can sprint faster than a cheetah with a rugby ball
I get annoyed sometimes and start to rage
Never mess with me
I make Lego creations piece by piece
When it falls down, I put it back up
I can run as fast as a lion
And I am always out of breath
I am as creative as a turtle
And as smart as a dolphin
This is me!

Thomas Rees (10)

Robert Gordon's College, Aberdeen

This Is Me

Although people spell it wrong
I'm Neil, this is me
I'm as intelligent as a quiz show
I will prove it time and time again
I have shiny brown hair
I'm large but I am proud of that
You could say I'm like a brown bear
I am as smart as can be
I love looking the part
I am an enthusiastic musician
My piano specifically
My world is filled with curiosity
With a microscope and telescope
So I can see things far and small
This is me
I am Neil.

Neil Rasalam (10)
Robert Gordon's College, Aberdeen

This Is Me!

This is me, Oscar
The colour of my eyes is sky-blue
I care about my family, all six of them
We love each other but we argue a lot
I swim a lot, Monday, Tuesday
Wednesday, Friday and Sunday
When I'm in the water
I'm as fast as a shark
When I'm in school, I try to work hard
But sometimes I'm as sleepy as a sloth
I hate veggies except for cucumbers
Which I eat every day
This is me, the one and only Oscar Jones
Once met, you can never forget.

Oscar Jones (10)
Robert Gordon's College, Aberdeen

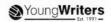

This Is Daniel

I am strong and brave
Just like a lion
I can swim so fast
Just like a dolphin

I am big and bold
That's so true
My strength is rugby
Away the ball flew

I love most music
I play the drums too
I know some songs
All the way through

I love reading comics
Marvel the most
I have quite a few
Not trying to boast

I have a great little sister
With bright blue eyes
But she can be annoying
When she cries.

Daniel Rose (10)

Robert Gordon's College, Aberdeen

All About Me

I am a football fan
An adventurous boy
A gamer
And lover of pizza

I have three pet fish
I'm a kind and caring kid
I have brown hair
And hazel eyes

I am a wolf, defensive in goals
I'm almost eleven years old
I am as funny as a frog
And I play many sports

I'm the biggest hater of getting out of bed
I've got a sister called Evie
When I'm older, I want to play for Liverpool
And finally a reading star.

Fraser Murphy (10)
Robert Gordon's College, Aberdeen

This Is Me

I'm Kristina
I'm as cool as an avocado
And I really love foxes
Gaming is my thing
And I play the violin
I have a pet cat
And she is really fat
I really enjoy swimming
Especially with my family
I have one eye of the ocean
And one eye of the field
With gold coin hair
I love to breathe in the cold winter air
My favourite colour is magenta purple
I love school, especially drama
But I can also be as lazy as a llama
This is me!

Kristina Krsmanovic (10)
Robert Gordon's College, Aberdeen

This Is Me

This is me, Harriet is my name
My furry friend, Bruno
Of course, comes cuddling up to play
A razor-sharp light runs through my stick
As I run to sweep the ball
I long to go to the stables to find my forever pony
I find have been riding for more than eight years
A blaze of light runs through my brush
As I sweep on the paper
I love to see my friends
I find they make me feel happy
I love my family, my mum, my dad
And even my sister
This is me!

Harriet Love (10)
Robert Gordon's College, Aberdeen

This Is Me

My name is Esme with two Es
I am really funny
I am a lightning bolt
Speeding down the field with my hockey stick
I am intelligent and energetic
If I was an animal, I would be a lion
I run with precision and speed
I'm like a busy bee, zooming in and out
I enjoy living the life with my friends
I hope it never ends
If I could be a weather, I would be the sun
It's jolly, it's bright and makes people smile
This is me, Esme with two Es.

Esme Rogers (10)
Robert Gordon's College, Aberdeen

This Is Me

This is me
Elizabeth or Lizzy with a Y
I'm not the tallest in the world
That doesn't help for netball
I really love my family
All of us wear glasses
An actress in the making is me
I can be someone else as I stand on the stage
I really like sport, especially ones with a bat
Walks are not my thing
They always go on forever
People say I'm a perfectionist
But I would say I wasn't
This is me, Elizabeth or Lizzy with a Y.

Elizabeth Webster (10)
Robert Gordon's College, Aberdeen

All About Me

You'll see me riding a wave
Or doing a backflip on the airmat
But not playing football
Because I don't like that

I named my dog Holly
Because she is extremely jolly
I kinda like my brother's cat
But not when he's killing a rat

I like to horse ride
And score a hockey goal with pride
I don't like caramel, it's too sweet for me
But spiders are just far too creepy
This is my poem all about me.

Hannah Cowie (10)
Robert Gordon's College, Aberdeen

This Is Me

My name is Maxwell Duncan
I go to Robert Gordon's College
That's where I get my knowledge
My hair is as brown as dark chocolate
Eyes the colour of hazelnuts
I want to be a farmer and drive tractors
in mud ruts
I play a lot of sport
Tennis on the court
On the ski slope, I'm as fast as a cheetah
I especially love rugby, playing with the ball
When I play football in defence
I'm as solid as a wall
This is me!

Maxwell Duncan (10)
Robert Gordon's College, Aberdeen

This Is Me!

I'm friendly and as fast as a cheetah
My favourite colour is turquoise
I'm not so skilled at dividing
My hobbies are hockey and netball
I'm normally the defender or goalie in netball
And a defender in hockey
I have crystal green eyes
And my hair is as blonde as a sunflower
I love animals, especially pandas
I also like my family and friends
My favourite subjects are writing and reading
I'm pretty lucky to be me!

Georgie Shepherd (10)
Robert Gordon's College, Aberdeen

This Is Me

I am Cameron
I am sociable
I am cool
I am silly
I am a pro gamer
I am super sporty
I am as fast as a cheetah
I am like a fish when swimming
I am a lover of animals
I am a lover of the rain
I am as smart as a calculator
I am good at laser run
I am not a fan of the sun
I am good at the aquathlon
I am excitable
I am passionate
I am a bit loud
I am awesome
I am a lover of family
This is me!

Cameron Jupp (10)
Robert Gordon's College, Aberdeen

This Is Me!

This is me...
I love my pets and all animals
Swimming four or five times a week
I am like a fish because of that
Some other hobbies include
Dancing like a ballerina
Twirling and running across the hockey field
Playing the guitar like a popstar
And reading like a bookworm
With my brown eyes, I see the world
I am as small as a poppy seed
Funny like a joke book
My descriptions could go on and on
This is me!

Poppy Walbaum (10)
Robert Gordon's College, Aberdeen

This Is Me

I am tall as a tree in a forest
But as quiet as a mouse
I am the youngest in my family
I love baking, that's no doubt
I am a bookworm but a sloth
Music, that's my thing
As loyal as a dog and good at listening
I'm as active as a bear hunting for a meal
I like to play tennis when I do, it gets real
I am as strong as a tiger
I do gymnastics too
My name is Caitlin
As happy as can be
This is me.

Caitlin Buckley (10)
Robert Gordon's College, Aberdeen

All About Me

I am a nature lover
I am a rugby star
I am a lover of dogs like dachshunds
I am a tiger, fierce and brave

My eyes are as blue as the sea
My hair is as blonde as sand
I am as tall as a giraffe
I am as happy as a frog

I have a hamster called Poppy
I am the youngest in the family
I love sports cars like Lamborghinis
I like race car drivers like Lando Norris
That's all about me.

Henry Johnston (10)
Robert Gordon's College, Aberdeen

This Is Me

I am small and kind
In maths, I use my mind
I am sporty and fun
Hockey and swimming are my number one
I enjoy drama and art
But my drawing isn't at the top of my chart
I care and love all my five pets
Hopefully, I don't have to take them to the vets
I like playing the chanter and pipes
It's great being in the band
I love all the hype
This is me, Lucia
Sometimes known as Lu-chichi.

Lucia Scrimgeour (10)
Robert Gordon's College, Aberdeen

This Is Me

Although I am as small as a snail
I'm as fast as a cheetah on my feet
My hair is as blonde
As gold shimmering in the sun
Rugby is my passion
Which makes me as tough as metal
Brussels sprouts I do not like
Thankfully, they only come on Christmas Eve night
Pizza, for me, is a yummy treat
Just like sweets only for me
I'm as helpful as a guide dog
This is me, I'm Ethan, friendly as can be.

Ethan Perry (9)
Robert Gordon's College, Aberdeen

This Is Me

I am Libby
I am happy and jolly like a dog
Sometimes as lazy as a sloth
But mostly as fast as a lightning bolt
Although I can be happy
I can also be quite sad
My favourite colours are yellow
And black like a bold bumblebee
I am very hyper when I'm at home
But at school, I'm as calm as a koala
Spicy food is my favourite
But I do not like nuts, not one bit
This is me!

Libby Black (9)
Robert Gordon's College, Aberdeen

This Is Me, Victor

My name is Victor, the football man
I am also a waffle fan
I have a cat who is pretty fast
In a race he will never be last

I love the planet which we live in
So let's put that plastic in the bin
I have chocolate hair
I am as strong as a bear

I speak French with my family
I like to think happily
I am good at being with trees
I like all insects, especially bees.

Victor Leroy (10)
Robert Gordon's College, Aberdeen

This Is Me

My name is Calum
I like to sleep all day
Unless I am out to play
All my friends are the best
but my sister can be a pest
I am fast and funny
And I love it when it's sunny
I am really sporty
And love to watch Rick and Morty
I am great at maths
But comprehension, not so fast
My eyes are like blue diamonds
Shining in the sky
And whatever I am
I am not shy.

Calum Kennedy (10)
Robert Gordon's College, Aberdeen

This Is Me

My name is Finn
I love football and I'm pretty tall
I love my family very much
I love food, my favourites are pizza and hot dogs
I may be a good goalkeeper
But I still run two-miles three times a week
As you probably know by now, I love football
But I also love video games
Such as Roblox, FIFA and Minecraft
I'm also very funny and energetic
And that's all about me.

Finn McCulloch (10)
Robert Gordon's College, Aberdeen

This Is Me

This is me
A future rugby player for Ireland
A comedian in the making
As fast as a flying bird
I run down the racing track
I am as short as a newly planted sapling
Every day, I practise rugby tackles in the garden
An actor, I dream to be
I have hazelnut hair
My eyes are blue, sharp and aware
I love my family so much, I swear
I am Struan, I am proud
This is me.

Struan McGurran (10)
Robert Gordon's College, Aberdeen

This Is Me

This is Alex, I am kind
I am helpful when you need it
My eyes are as brown as wood
I am a bookworm reading books
I am as happy as a day
With a red juicy strawberry
I am as warm as the sun
But love the snow
I am full of cheers and laughter
As I play with my friends and family
I am the blue sky all around you
I am a football fan cheering
This is me, Alex.

Alex Dospinescu (10)
Robert Gordon's College, Aberdeen

This Is Me

My name is Quentin Booth
I'm as strong as a sabretooth
The day of my birthday
Is the 20th May
My favourite animal is a kangaroo
I also like koalas too
I'm as happy as a flower
My blinding smile will make you cower
I'm a massive rugby fan
I go to Murrayfield whenever I can
I am a really cool dude
Spaghetti is my favourite food
This is me!

Quentin Booth (10)

Robert Gordon's College, Aberdeen

This Is Me

I'm as fast as a cheetah
I pounce like a lion
I can give you a fright
That scares you in the night
My eyes are hazelnuts
I've got brownish hair
I look like my mum
I'm in a fantastic family of four
I love going to Denmark to see my relatives
I try hard for my hockey team
I was born in enjoyable England
But I love it here in stunning Scotland.

Smilla Addison (10)
Robert Gordon's College, Aberdeen

This Is Me

This is me, Jack
brown hair, brown eyes
I am as sleepy as a sloth
But as energetic as an excited toddler
I am like a kangaroo
when I do my hobbies on a trampoline
I am as fast as a cheetah
As I tackle the crowd of the playground
I have an annoying little goblin as my sister
As she scrummages around the house
annoying me
This is me
I am Jack!

Jack Bradley (9)
Robert Gordon's College, Aberdeen

This Is Me!

It's me, Freddie with an IE
A towering giant hiding in the trees
Never defiant
But not a friend to the bees
Riding down the trails
I love mountain biking
Running down the rugby field
It's something that I'm liking
Living the dream with my amazing friends
This story is a good one
I hope it never ends
This is me, Freddie with an IE.

Freddie Findlay (10)
Robert Gordon's College, Aberdeen

This Is Me

I'll skate and skate and skate
I'll jump and spin
I'll twirl and I'll fall and fall
But I'll keep getting up
Until I've had enough
That is what I love

I'll punch and box
I'll kick and cross
I'll miss and miss
And I'll duck and duck
Until I've had enough
That is what I love
This is me!

Celeste Tait (10)
Robert Gordon's College, Aberdeen

This Is Me

I am...
As fast as a cheetah
As strong as a lion
As sad as a raven
As happy as a llama
As quiet as a tiger
As loud as a puppy
As sleek as a snake
As clumsy as a chick
As fast as lightning
As warm as the sun
As cold as ice
As smart as an owl
As energetic as a lioness
As fierce as a wolf
As busy as a bee
This is me!

Ailie McIntosh (10)
Robert Gordon's College, Aberdeen

This Is Me

This is me, Blair
I have thick brown hair,
And sparkling hazel eyes.
I am as crafty as a beaver,
My artwork, delicate in detailed colour
Homework is not a favourite of mine.
However, I do love rugby,
It makes you tough as nails.
Skiing down the ski slope at supersonic speed
A good skier I hope to be.
This is me
Blair, the one and only.

Blair Cowie (10)

Robert Gordon's College, Aberdeen

This Is Me

I am as strong as a tiger
And as flexible as a snake
I am as messy as a monkey
And I love baking cakes
I am as curious as a dog
But not as patient as a cat
I am as tall as a giraffe
And I like walking on paths
I am as energetic as a frog
And as fast as a tiger
I am as sleepy as a sloth
But I like Scotch broth
This is me!

Leah Robertson (10)
Robert Gordon's College, Aberdeen

This Is Me, Oscar

I'm a penguin lover
Ice cream is the best
Katsu curry is next
I am the oldest child

Wasps are the worst by far
Seagulls steal my snacks
I like warm weather beaches
Caramel is nice

My mum and dad are the best
I love mountain biking
I love animals
After Eights are good
This is me!

Oscar Noble (10)
Robert Gordon's College, Aberdeen

This Is Me, Harris

I love wearing glasses
Inside my school classes
I dislike walking my dog
In the bog

I am crazy
Definitely not lazy
My eyes are the colour of the sky
So I can see all the birds that fly

I jump like a bunny
So I'm very funny
I am loud
But also proud.

Harris Mowat (10)
Robert Gordon's College, Aberdeen

This Is Me

My name is Ruppy
I'm told I'm very funny
I like to build with Lego
I have an extreme level of creativeness
I'm so curious, I once touched a nettle
I like weapon games on Roblox
I'm as smart as a calculator
I have phobias that make me very unique
This is me.

Rupanjon Banik (10)
Robert Gordon's College, Aberdeen

This Is Me!

My name is Aston
I am as funny as a clownfish
Lots of cool friends too
My favourite sports are boxing, golf and go-karting
In class, I am very chatty
I am as competitive as a lion
I love going to school and seeing all my friends
I am as curious as a puppy dog
This is me!

Aston Sharp (10)
Robert Gordon's College, Aberdeen

YOUNG WRITERS INFORMATION

We hope you have enjoyed reading this book – and that you will continue to in the coming years.

If you're the parent or family member of an enthusiastic poet or story writer, do visit our website **www.youngwriters.co.uk/subscribe** and sign up to receive news, competitions, writing challenges and tips, activities and much, much more! There's lots to keep budding writers motivated!

If you would like to order further copies of this book, or any of our other titles, then please give us a call or order via your online account.

Young Writers
Remus House
Coltsfoot Drive
Peterborough
PE2 9BF
(01733) 890066
info@youngwriters.co.uk

Join in the conversation!
Tips, news, giveaways and much more!

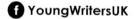 **YoungWritersUK** 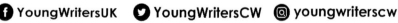 **YoungWritersCW** 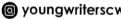 **youngwriterscw**